CREATURES
GREAT
and Small

J a n   G o d f r e y   a n d   G a i l   Y e r r i l l

CONTENTS

Creatures great and small 6

The serpent who spoke 8

The creatures who floated 10

The frogs who came out of the sky 12

The ravens who helped 14

The sea creature who hiccupped 16

The fierce and growly lions 18

The very first Christmas 20

The camels who travelled by night 22

The donkey who carried a king 24

The cockerel who crowed 26

The fish who nearly weren't there 28

Creatures great and small

A long time ago and far, far away, God made a beautiful world.

God loved the mountains and the streams and the sweet-smelling blossom on the new leafy trees.

So God filled the mountains with all sorts of creatures and the streams with all sorts of fish.

God made lions and tigers and bears and giraffes; reindeer and antelopes; parrots and wrens; rabbits and foxes.

There were tall creatures and stripy creatures. Some had swishy tails, some had tickly whiskers and some had funny faces.

Some made growly noises, some sang chirpy songs and some made no sound at all.

God saw that everything he had made was very good—but something was missing. God made people too, so that they could be his friends.

7

The serpent who spoke

A long time ago and far, far away, Adam and Eve were God's friends. They looked after a beautiful garden that God had made.

'You may eat anything you like,' God said, 'except the fruit from the tree in the middle of the garden.'

The fruit was shining and ripe, glossy and gleaming and juicy.

A slippery serpent appeared in the garden, all coiled and slithery. Its tongue was quick and forked.

'Go on…' hissed the serpent. 'It looks sssssssssso good.'

'God said we mustn't,' said Eve.

'You'll be as clever as God if you eat it,' whispered the serpent. 'Go on…'

Eve took a bite and gave some to Adam. But then—

Adam and Eve weren't happy at all. They felt ashamed and they hid.

'Why are you hiding?' God asked Adam and Eve. 'Did you eat the fruit from the tree in the middle of the garden?'

'It wasn't my fault—Eve gave it to me,' said Adam.

'It wasn't my fault—the serpent told me to,' said Eve.

'Our friendship is spoiled,' said God. 'Couldn't you trust me for all the good things you needed?'

The serpent crawled away into the undergrowth and God sent Adam and Eve away from the beautiful garden for ever.

The creatures who floated

A long time ago and far, far away, there lived a man called Noah.

'It's going to rain very hard,' God said to Noah, 'and there will be a flood. I want you to build a big boat—an ark—to keep everyone safe and dry. Take your family into the ark with every kind of creature, two by two by two.'

So Noah built an ark with lots of hammering and banging. Then all the creatures went into the ark, two by two by two.

Then down came the rain: spots and drops and splashes of rain; pools and puddles and rivers of rain; lakes and seas and floods of rain.

The trees and the mountain tops disappeared, but Noah's ark floated on top of the wet and wavy water. And Noah and his family and all the creatures stayed safe and dry inside.

When the rain stopped raining and the floodwaters went down, mountains and hills and leafy trees appeared again.

'You can come out of the ark now,' said God to Noah. And then… Noah and the animals had a big surprise. A beautiful, bright rainbow filled the sky.

'There'll never be a big flood like this again,' said God. 'I promise.'

The frogs who came out of the sky

A long time ago and far, far away, God's people lived in Egypt.
The king of Egypt grew afraid of them because there were
so many. So he was cruel to them and made them his slaves.

God sent Moses to the king.

'God says, "Let my people go so they can be free."'

'No!' said the king. 'I don't know your God.
I won't listen to him.'

'OK,' said Moses. 'God has given you a
chance to listen and you have decided
to ignore him. It's your choice.'

Then the river turned yukky so no
one could use the water.

There were crowds of hoppy frogs
that came out of the sky like rain!

The frogs jumped out of the river into the houses.
They hopped into the bedrooms and cupboards and shoes.
They jumped into the kitchens and ovens and cooking pots
and baking pans and jars!

'Take these frogs away!' said the king to Moses.

Moses prayed to God and the frogs went away. But as
soon as they went, the king was cruel and unkind again.
Then there were buzzy insects and lots more nasty things
before the king finally let God's people go free.

Then Moses led God's people out of Egypt to a land of
their own.

The ravens
who helped

A long time ago and far, far away,
God sent Elijah to speak to King Ahab.
   'Listen to God's message,' said Elijah.
'It won't rain today and it won't rain tomorrow.
It won't rain again until you remember who the
true and living God is. It will be a hungry, dry
and dusty time. There'll be nothing to eat and
nothing to drink.'
   Elijah didn't wait to find out how angry that
made the king!

'There's a little stream over there
where you will find water to drink,'
God told Elijah.
　　Elijah found the little stream of
running water.
　　Then God spoke to the ravens that cawed
and called and wheeled and watched, and
they took Elijah bread and meat every morning and
evening, breakfast and supper, until the stream dried up.
　　God took care of Elijah until the time came when rain
fell once more on the land.

The sea creature who hiccupped

A long time ago and far, far away, God sent Jonah
to see the wicked people who lived in Nineveh.

'Tell them to stop doing cruel and unkind things,' said God.

But Jonah didn't want to go. He sailed on a big boat,
over the seas and far away.

Then a big storm came. The wind howled and the waves
tossed the boat up and down, up and down.

'Throw me over the side!' shouted Jonah. 'I should have
listened to God. Throw me into the big, wild sea and
everything will be all right.'

Down, down, down went Jonah and the sea became
calm again. Up, up, up came a very large sea creature who
swallowed Jonah in one big gulp!

Then, after three days and three nights, the sea creature hiccupped SO loudly that Jonah popped out of the sea creature's jaws like a cork out of a bottle.

When God spoke to Jonah again, he went to Nineveh. The people listened to God's message. Then they told God they were sorry. And because God is good and kind and loving and forgiving, God forgave them.

The fierce and growly lions

A long time ago and far, far away, there lived a man called Daniel. Daniel knew that God was great and good and very special, and he prayed to him three times every day.

The king's men didn't like Daniel. So they tried to trick him.

They persuaded the king to pass a law so that anyone who prayed to anyone at all except the king would be thrown to the lions.

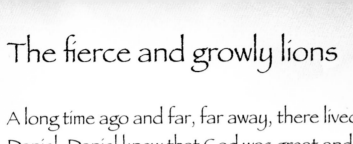

The trick worked. Daniel prayed to God just the same.

'Daniel thinks his God is better than you, O King,' said the king's men. 'Daniel must be thrown to the lions!'

Now the king was worried. After all, lions are rather fierce and growly. But Daniel was thrown into the lions' den that very night, at supper time!

The king went to the lions' den very early in the morning.

'O King, live for ever!' said Daniel. 'You didn't need to worry. God sent an angel to look after me, and here I am.'

'Daniel's God is the true and living God,' said the king. 'He can save—even from the mouths of growly lions.'

The very first Christmas

A long time ago and far, far away, Jesus was born in Bethlehem.

A dozy donkey was snuffling, the ox was fidgeting, a goat was munching—as goats usually do.

And there was Mary, cradling her new-born child. She wrapped him up warmly and placed him in the manger, which was filled with hay.

Why would there be visitors in the
stable that night?

Sleepy shepherds had been
looking after their sheep when angels
had appeared, filling the night sky
with bright and beautiful light!

'Go to Bethlehem!' they had been
told. So here they were, looking
for a baby in a manger, for the
son of God, for Jesus born that
night—the child who would one
day bring peace to the world.

The camels who travelled by night

A long time ago and far, far away, wise men from the east saw a beautiful new star in the heavens.

'It must be a sign,' they said.

'A new king has been born,' they said.

'We must go to worship him,' they said.

So they woke their camels, and packed their bags for a long journey, over the desert sands. They packed special gifts for the baby king they hoped to find.

Every night the camels plodded steadily through the darkness as they followed the star in the heavens. Every day they rested from their dusty journey.

They stopped in Jerusalem—but the baby king wasn't born in the palace. So they followed the star onwards to a little house in Bethlehem, where they found Mary holding Jesus, her little son.

The men climbed down from their camels and brought their gifts to Jesus—gold, frankincense and myrrh. Then they knelt and worshipped God's son, the king born to the Jewish people.

The donkey who carried a king

A long time ago and far, far away, there was a young, frisky donkey, marked with a shape like a cross over his back.

One day little donkey watched as two men untied him and spread their cloaks on his back. They took him to see another man, a man with rough hands and kind eyes.

No one had ever sat on his back before, but the man with kind eyes climbed on to little donkey's back. He spoke quietly and calmly to little donkey.

As little donkey began to trot along the road, people started to cheer and wave palm branches in the air. They threw their cloaks on the road, making a soft path for him.

'It's the man who makes the blind see,' someone said.

'It's the man who calmed a storm,' said someone else.

'He heals anyone who needs his help,' said another.

'Look, it's Jesus! Hooray!' shouted the children.

'Welcome, King Jesus!'

Then little donkey realised that the man with kind eyes riding on his back was...
a king!

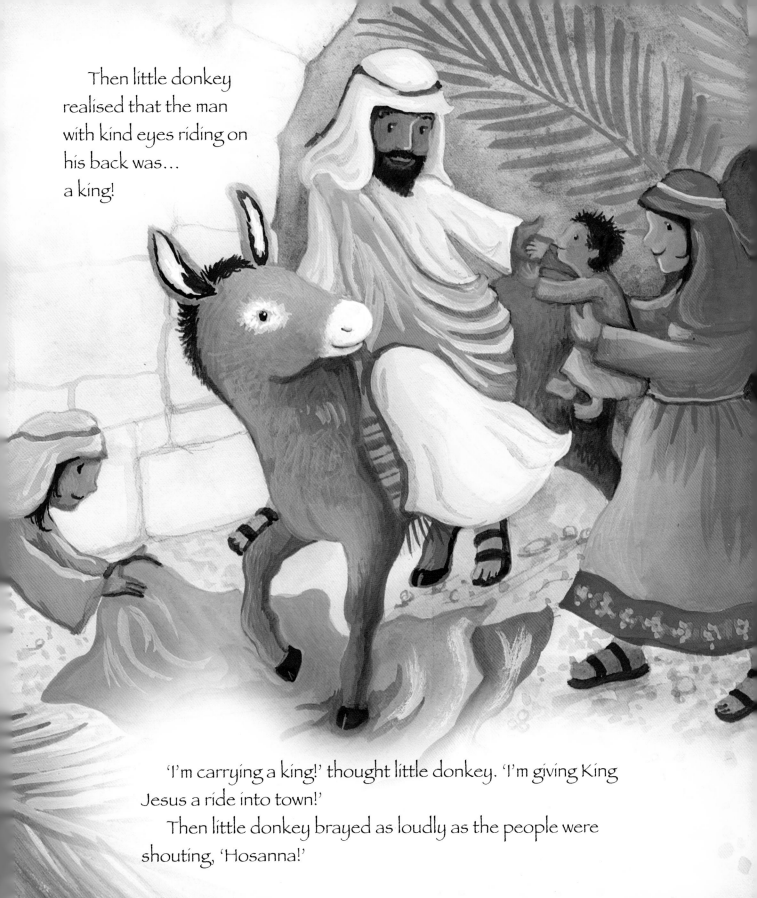

'I'm carrying a king!' thought little donkey. 'I'm giving King Jesus a ride into town!'
Then little donkey brayed as loudly as the people were shouting, 'Hosanna!'

The cockerel who crowed

A long time ago and far, far away, a cockerel plumped out his feathers and closed his eyes. He didn't know that there was a man eating his last supper with his friends that night.

'I know I'm your friend,' said Jesus to Peter. 'But before the cockerel crows, you will tell people three times that you don't even know me.'

'Never!' said Peter. 'You're my best friend.'

Jesus had many friends. But there were some people who didn't like Jesus at all. One night they marched Jesus away into the darkness.

Now Peter was waiting while Jesus was questioned.

'You know that man Jesus, don't you?' a girl said.

'Me? Not me,' said Peter, moving away.

'That man was with Jesus,' she said, pointing.

'No,' said Peter. 'I don't know him at all.'

Then the men came up to Peter in the shadows.

'You even talk like Jesus,' they said.

'No,' said Peter. 'NO! NO! NO!'

And then the cockerel spoke, as the sky was changing to a new rose-pink morning.

'Cock-a-doodle-doooo! Cock-a-doodle-doooo!'

Then Peter remembered what Jesus had said. Peter had never been so sad in all his life.

The fish who nearly weren't there

A long time ago and far, far away, Jesus was crucified
on a wooden cross. His friends could not believe it when
he died. But they could hardly believe their eyes when
God brought him back to life.

At first they saw him every day, but they were sad when they
didn't see Jesus for a while.

'I'm going fishing,' said Peter.

'We'll come too,' said his friends.

So they went out in a boat and they fished all night long.
But they didn't catch any fish at all! Not one.

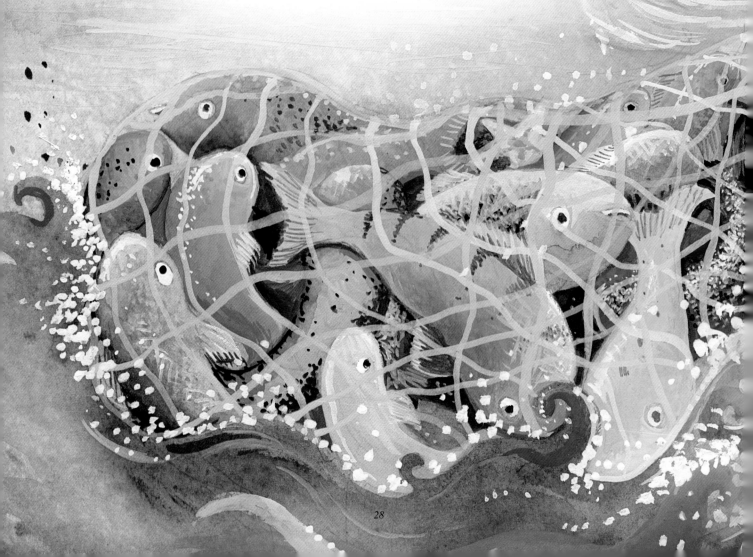

When the sun rose, the friends heard a voice.

'Haven't you caught any fish?' called a man from the edge
of the water.

'No, nothing at all,' the friends called back.

'Try again,' said the man. 'Put your net out on the other side.'
So they threw the net out one last time...

And suddenly it grew heavy with... FISH! Wriggly,
flapping fish; big and shiny and wet and gleaming fish,
fresh from the sea.

Peter jumped into the water. He knew the man was Jesus!

The others dragged in the huge net of fish.

'Bring some of the fish you've just caught,' said Jesus to his
friends.

Then the fishermen shared a breakfast of fish and bread
with Jesus, amazed at what they'd caught—the fish who nearly
weren't there.